****

WHO'S IN CHARGE HERE? 1996

****

Gerald Gardner

DOVE
BOOKS

ISBN 0-7871-1300-X

Printed in the United States of America

Dove Books
8955 Beverly Boulevard
Los Angeles, CA 90048

Distributed by Penguin USA

Interior layout by Carolyn Wendt
Cover design and layout by Rick Penn-Kraus
Photos courtesy of Bettmann Newsphotos, Wide World,
The White House, Smithsonian Institute, Movie Star News

First Printing: October 1996

10 9 8 7 6 5 4 3 2 1

For Emma Nestle Gardner

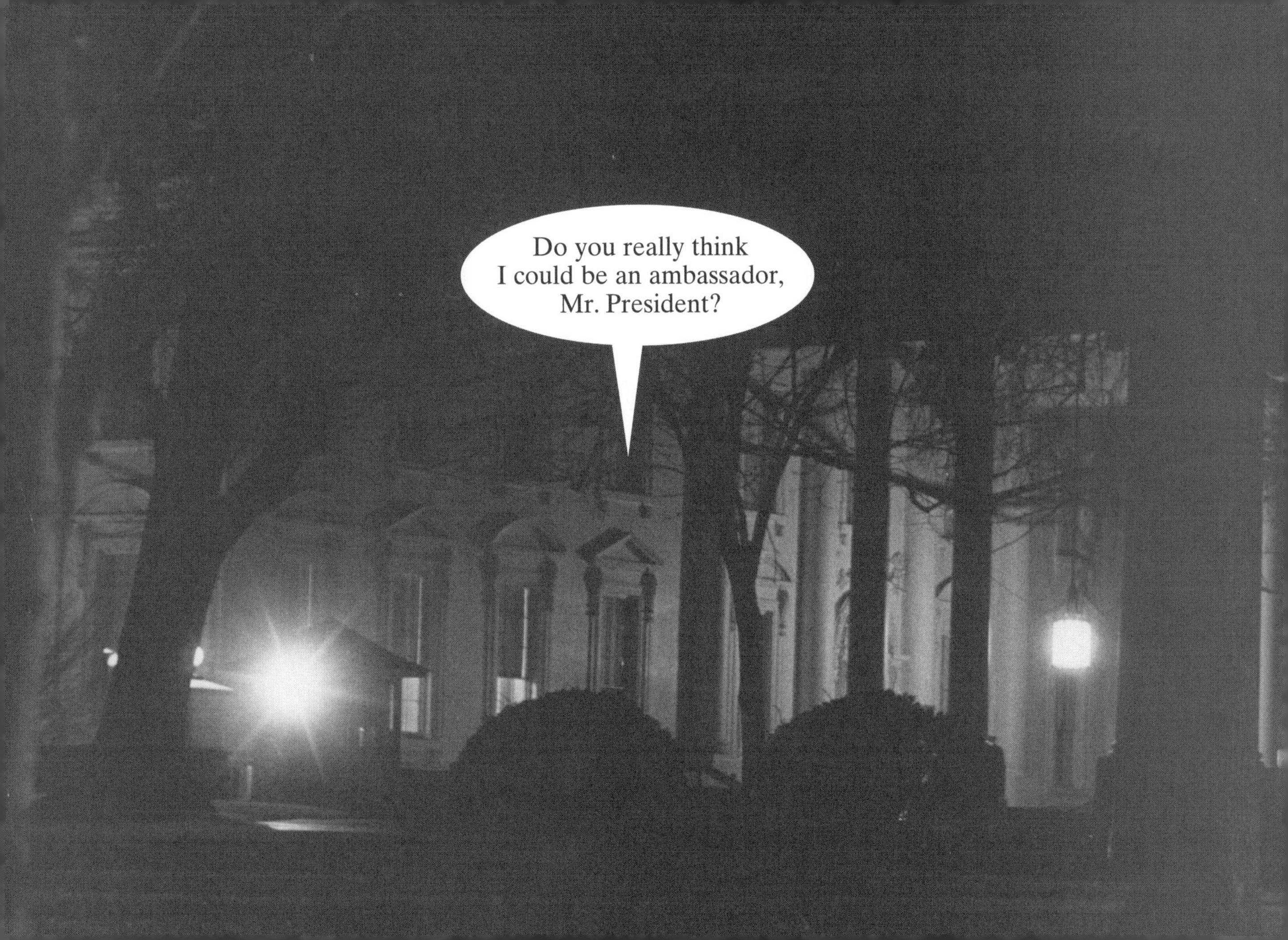
Do you really think I could be an ambassador, Mr. President?

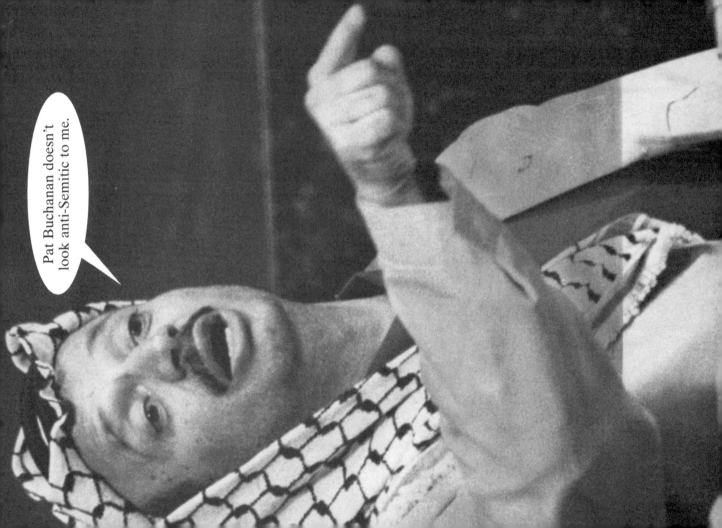

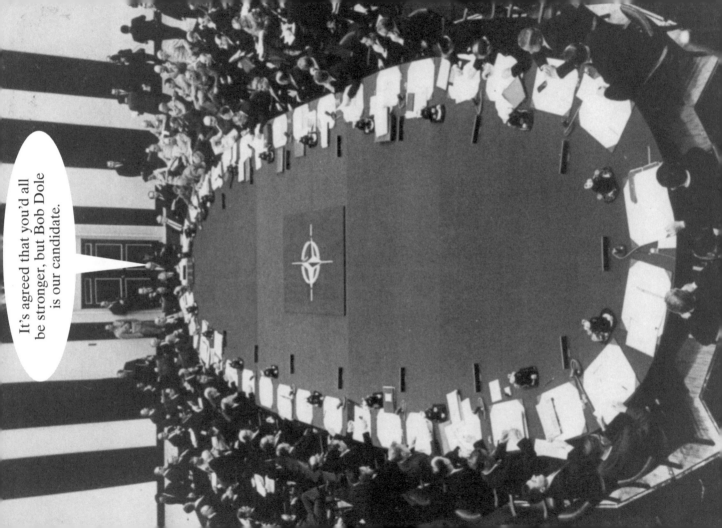

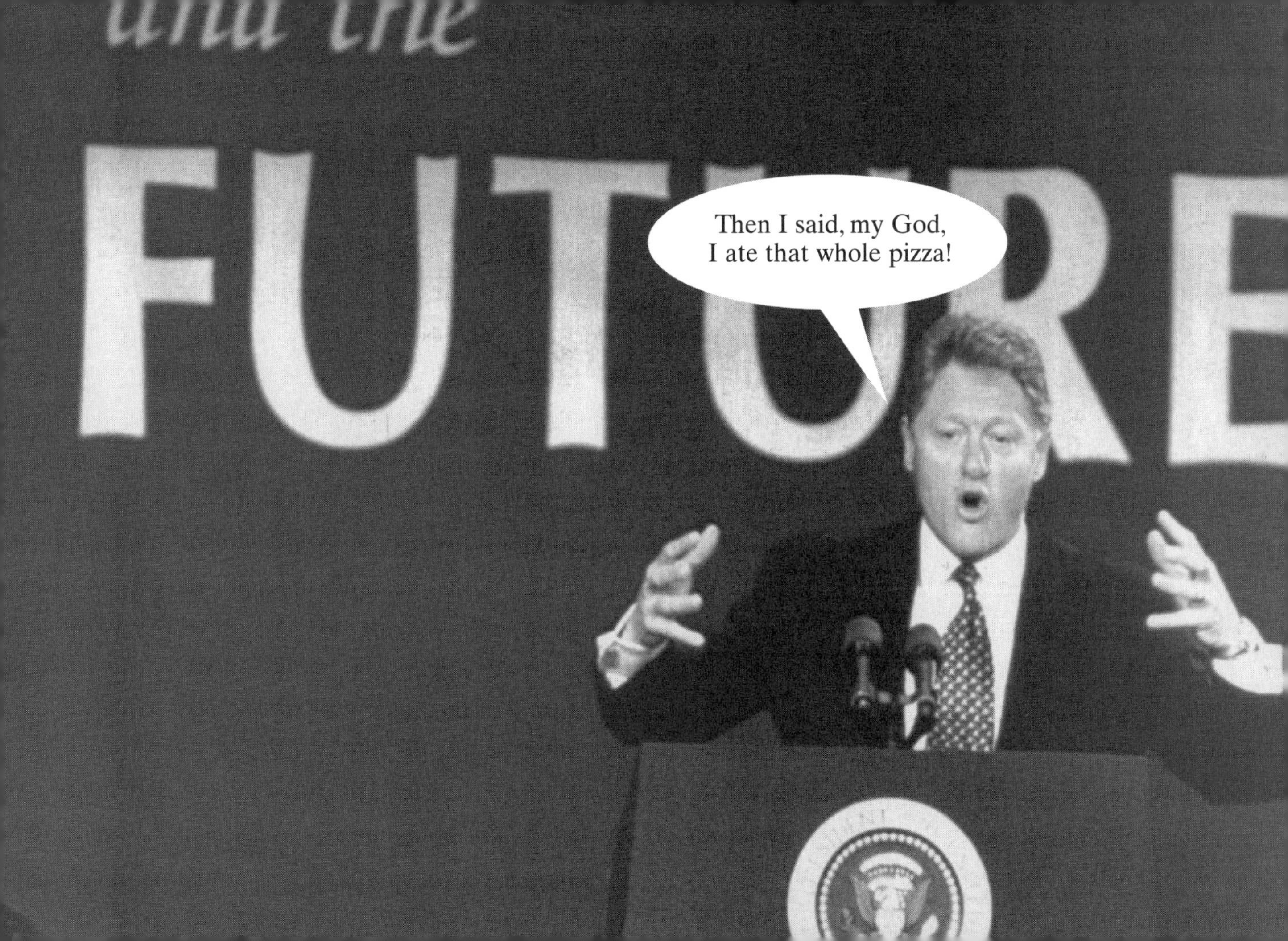
FUTURE
Then I said, my God, I ate that whole pizza!